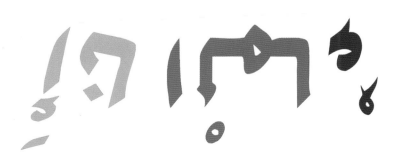

Text copyright © 1996 by Jean Marzollo.
Illustrations copyright © 1996 by Judith Moffatt.

First printing, July 1996
All rights reserved. Published by Scholastic Inc.
SCHOLASTIC, and associated logos are trademarks
and/or registered trademarks of Scholastic Inc.

ISBN 978-0-439-86378-0

First Arabic Edition, 2006. Printed in China.

1 2 3 4 5 6 7 8 9 10 62 11 10 09 08 07

أَنا الْماءُ

تَأْليفُ: جين مارزوﻟّو • رُسومُ: جوديث موفات

ܝܰܥܢܝܼܬ ܚܛܝܼ ܚܘ݂

ܝܼܡܩܐ ܚܘ݂

ܬܚ ܡܢܩܐ܂

ﺑَﺮْﺩٌ ﻗَﺎﺭِﺱٌ ﻓِﻲ ﺍﻟْﺒَﺮّ.

ᑲᑐᖅ ᖃᐅᒪᔪᕐᒥᒃ ᓇᓂᓯᑐᐃᓐᓇᓚᐅᖅᐳᖅ.

لَيْسُوا كَثِيراً جِدّاً هُنا.

ܝܶܬ ܩܶܢܝܶܬ ܪܕܬܶܢܝܺܢ ܩܶܘܢܶܓܶܪ ܬܶܝܘ܆

إذا أردتُ أن أصبحَ ملكاً صغيراً.

ܫܟܝܪܘܬܗ ܠܗ ܐ
ܘܡܫܪ ܗܘ ܒܝܬܗ ܠܗ ܘܬܗ

دَاسَتْ بِسْيَارْ كُوجِيلَنْ وَارِي حِكَايَةَ إِي.

وَإِذَا بِالطَّائِرِ يَنْقَضُّ عَلَى السَّمَكَةِ.

ܝܸܥܪܘܼܣܩ ܚܵܐ ܠܝܼܚܸܢ ܚܠ.

أَنا أَمْواجٌ لِلْمُشاهَدَةِ.

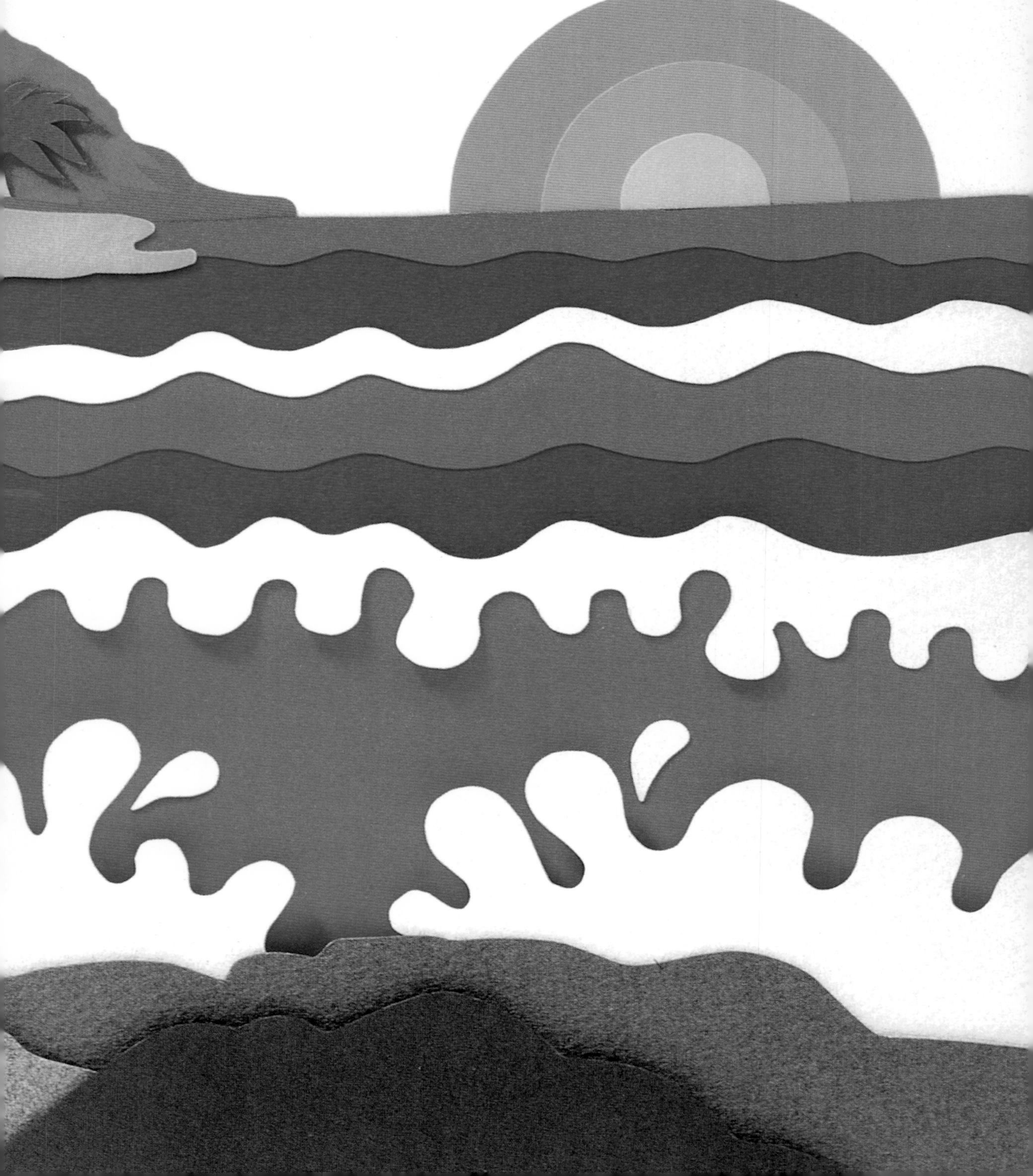

أَنا كُلُّ تِلْكَ الأُمورِ،
لا بَلْ أَنا أَكْثَرُ.

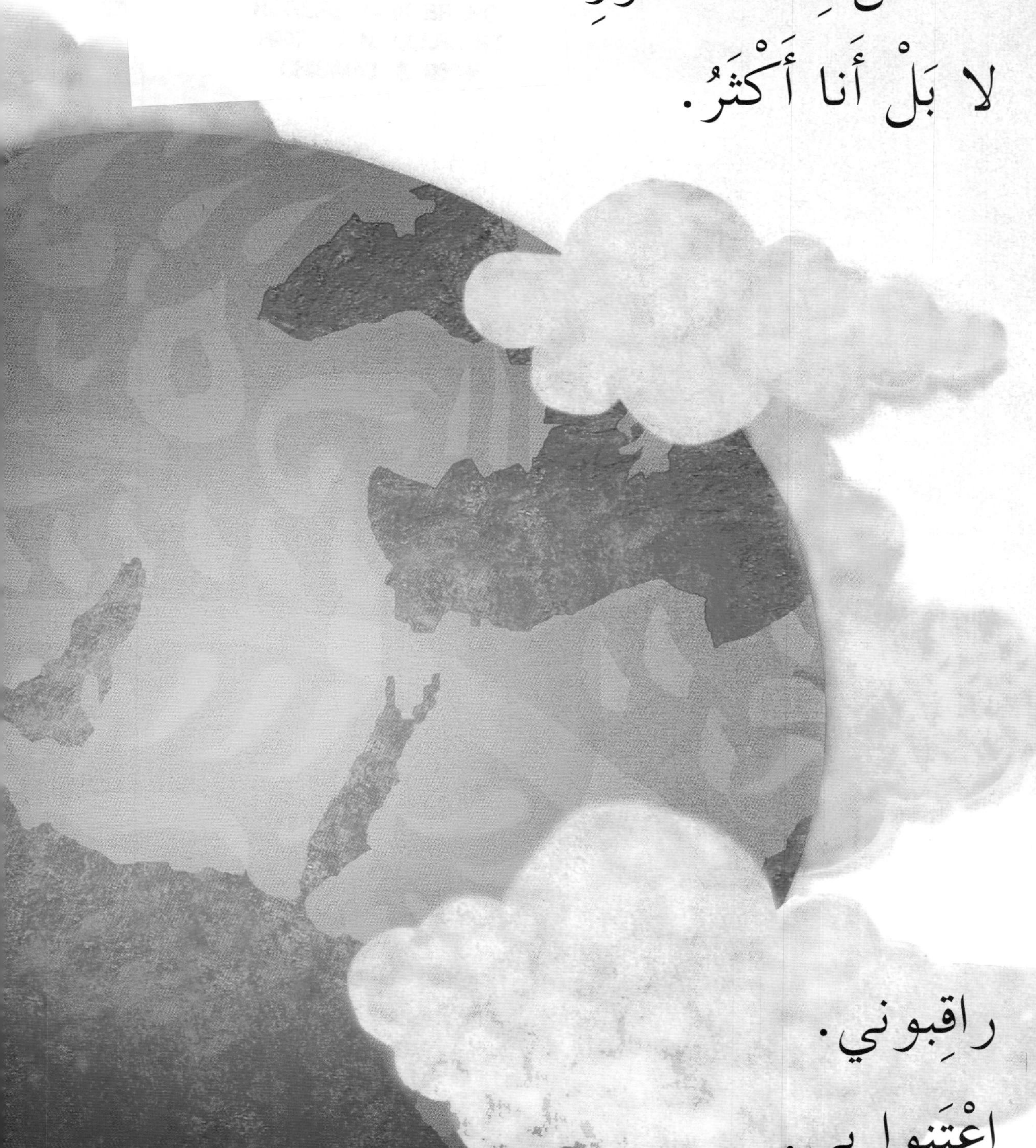

راقِبوني.
اِعْتَنوا بي.
أَنا الْماءُ.